oasis | STOP THE CLOCKS

CW00549201

WISE PUBLICATIONS
part of The Music Sales Group
London/New York/Paris/Sydney/Copenhagen/Berlin/Madrid/Tokyo

PUBLISHED BY

WISE PUBLICATIONS
14-15 BERNERS STREET, LONDON W1T 3LJ, UK.

EXCLUSIVE DISTRIBUTORS:

MUSIC SALES LIMITED
DISTRIBUTION CENTRE, NEWMARKET ROAD,
BURY ST EDMUNDS, SUFFOLK IP33 3YB, UK.

MUSIC SALES PTY LIMITED
120 ROTHSCHILD AVENUE, ROSEBERY,
NSW 2018, AUSTRALIA.

ORDER NO. AM988020
ISBN 1-84609-806-8
THIS BOOK © COPYRIGHT 2006 WISE PUBLICATIONS,
A DIVISION OF MUSIC SALES LIMITED.

ARTWORK © PETER BLAKE. LICENSED BY DACS 2006.
ORIGINAL SLEEVE ART DIRECTION BY NOEL GALLAGHER & SIMON HALFON.
PHOTOGRAPHY BY LAWRENCE WATSON.

PRINTED IN THE EU.

WWW.MUSICSALES.COM

Rock 'n' Roll Star

Words & Music by Noel Gallagher

The day's mov-ing just____ too fast____ for me.

I need some time in the sun - shine,

I got - ta slow it right down.____ The day's mov-ing just____

____ too fast____ for me. I

real far,_____ you're not con - cerned_____ a - bout the

way we are._____ In my mind_____ my dreams_____ are real,_____

are you con - cerned a - bout the way I feel?_____ To - night_____

_____ I'm a rock 'n' roll_____ star.

I am,— look at you now, you're all in my hands— to-night.—

D.%. al Coda

To - night—

12

13

Some Might Say

Words & Music by Noel Gallagher

1. Some might say — that sun-shine fol-lows thun-der
(Verse 2 see block lyric)

go and tell — it to — the man — who can - not shine.

Some might say — that

we should ne-ver pon-der on our thoughts to-day 'cause they hold sway ov-er time.

Some might say we will find a bright-er day.

Some might say we will find

gain. ____

The sink is full of fish-es 'cause

she's got dir-ty dish-es on the brain. ____

{ It was

ov-er-flow-ing gent-ly   but it's all e-le-men-tary my

And my dog's been itch-ing,   itch-ing in the kitch-en once a-

1.

friend. ____

gain. ____

Verse 2:
Some might say they don't believe in heaven
Go and tell it to the man who lives in hell
Some might say you get what you've been given
If you don't get yours I won't get mine as well.

Talk Tonight

Words & Music by Noel Gallagher

1. Sit - tin' on my own, chew - in' on a bone a thou - sand mil - lion miles_
(Verse 2 see block lyric)

I wan - na talk to - night,_____ un - til the morn - in' light,_____ 'bout how you saved my life,_____

{ and you and me_____ see how we are,_____
  I wan - na_____ talk to -

you and me_____ see how we are._____

Verse 2:
All your dreams are made of strawberry lemonade,
And you make sure I eat today.
Take me walking
To where you played when you were young.
I'll never say that I won't ever make you cry,
And this I'll say I don't know why.
I know I'm leavin'
But I'll be back another day.

Lyla

Words & Music by Noel Gallagher

The Importance Of Being Idle

Words & Music by Noel Gallagher

1. I sold my soul for the se -
*2° Instrumental till ***
(3.) lost my faith in the sum -

34

Wonderwall

Words & Music by Noel Gallagher

I don't be-lieve that an-y-bo-dy feels the way I do a-bout you now.

1. Back-beat the word was on the street that the fire in your heart is out.
(Verse 2 see block lyric)

I'm sure you've heard it all be-fore but you nev-er real-ly had a doubt.

I don't be - lieve___ that an - y - bo - dy feels the way I do___ a - bout you now.___

And all___

___ the roads___ we have___ to walk___ are wind - ing and all___

___ the lights___ that lead___ us there___ are blind - ing.

There are ma - ny things— that I—— would like to say to you— but I don't know how,—

be - cause
I said

may - be—— you're gon - na be the one that

saves me,—— and af - ter all——

Verse 2:
Today was gonna be the day
But they'll never throw it back to you
By now you should've somehow
Realised what you're not to do
I don't believe that anybody
Feels the way I do
About you now.

And all the roads that lead you there were winding
And all the lights that light the way are blinding
There are many things that I would like to say to you
But I don't know how.

Slide Away

Words & Music by Noel Gallagher

43

Verse 2:
Hold me now, all the world's asleep.
I need you now, you've knocked me off my feet.
I dream of you, and we talk of growing old.
But you said, please don't!

Cigarettes & Alcohol

Words & Music by Noel Gallagher

1. Is it my—
(Verse 2 see block lyric)

-pen,_____ you got-ta make it hap - pen,_____

you got-ta make it hap - pen,_____ you got-ta make it hap-

-pen._____

you got-ta make it hap -

Verse 2:
Is it worth the aggravation
To find yourself a job
When there's nothing worth working for?
It's a crazy situation
But all I need
Are cigarettes and alcohol.

The Masterplan

Words & Music by Noel Gallagher

Take the time to make some sense of what you want to say. and

Say it loud___ and sing it proud___ to-day.___

2.

mas - - - ter - plan.

Verse 2:
I'm not saying right is wrong
It's up to us to make
The best of all the things that come our way
'Cos everything that's been has passed
The answer's in the looking glass
There's four and twenty million doors
On life's endless corridor
Say it loud and sing it proud and they will.

Dance if you wanna dance, *etc.*

Live Forever

Words & Music by Noel Gallagher

1, 2, 4. May - be___ I don't real - ly want to know how your gar - den grows, I___ just want_ to fly.___ Late - ly___ did you ev - er feel the pain in the mor - ing rain as it soaks_ you to the bone?_

58

Gon- na live for- ev - er. _____

Gon- na live for- ev -

- er. _____

Chorus 2:
Maybe I will never be
All the things that I want to be.
Now is not the time to cry,
Now's the time to find out why.
I think you're the same as me,
We see things they'll never see,
You and I are gonna live forever.

Acquiesce

Words & Music by Noel Gallagher

sleep in - side,____ I on-ly wan-na see the light that

shines be - hind____ your eyes._____ I

hope that I can say the things I wish I'd said,____ to

sing my soul to sleep and take me back to bed,____ you

61

soul._ Be-cause we need____ each oth- er, we be- lieve____

____ in one an-oth- er, and I know we're____ gon- na un-cov-

-er, what's sleep-ing in__ our soul._ What's sleep-ing in our

soul._____

Verse 2:
There are many things that I would like to know,
And there are many places that I wish to go,
But everything's depending on the way the wind may blow.

I don't know what it is that makes me feel alive,
I don't know how to wake the things that sleep inside,
I only wanna see the light that shines behind your eyes.

Supersonic

Words & Music by Noel Gallagher

1. I need to be my-self,
(Verse 2 see block lyric)
I can't be no one else,
no one else,
I'm feel - ing su - per - so - nic, give—

Verse 2:
You need to be yourself,
You can't be no one else.
I know a girl called Elsa,
She's into Alka Seltzer
She sniffs it through a cane
On a supersonic train.

And she makes me laugh,
I got her autograph.
She done it with a doctor
On a helicopter,
She's sniffing in her tissue
Selling the Big Issue.

And she finds out…

Half The World Away

Words & Music by Noel Gallagher

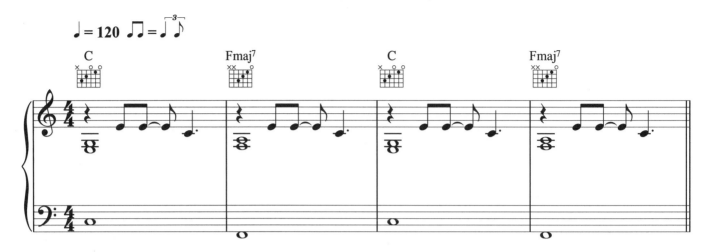

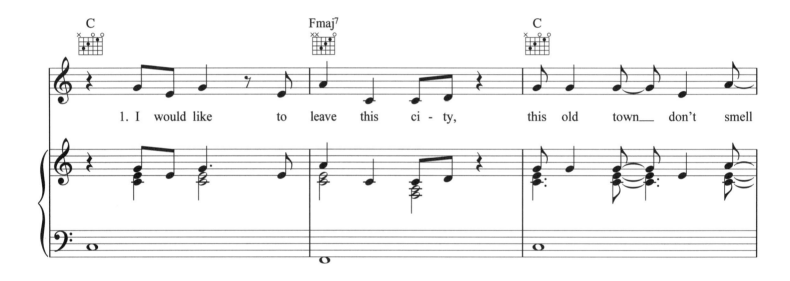

1. I would like to leave this ci - ty, this old town___ don't smell

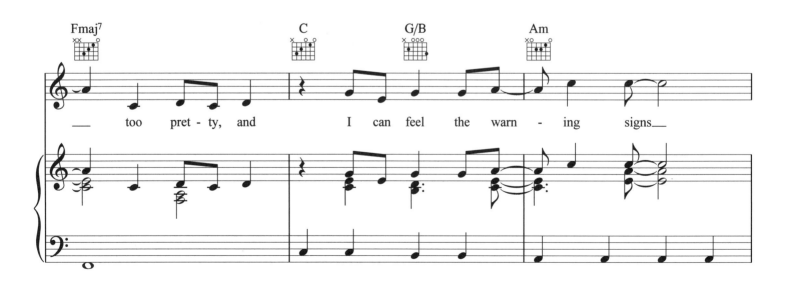

___ too pret - ty, and I can feel the warn - ing signs___

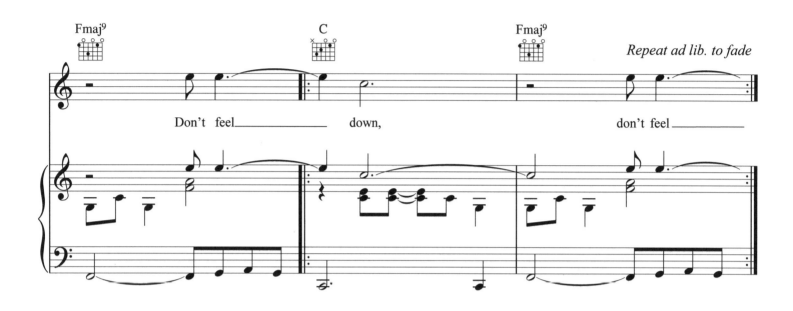

Don't feel_____ down,   don't feel_____

Verse 2:
And when I leave this planet
You know I'd stay but I just can't stand it,
And I can feel the warning signs
Running around my mind.
And if I could leave this spirit,
I'll find me a hole and I'll live in it,
And I can feel the warning signs
Running around my mind.

Go Let It Out

Words & Music by Noel Gallagher

like your-self— a lot, go let it out,_____ go let it in,_____

_____ and go let it out. *Spoken:* (Pick up the bass)

2. Life is pre - co - cious in the most pe - cu - liar way,_____
(Verse 3 see block lyric)

sis - ter psy - cho - sis, don't got a lot— to say. She go let it out,_____

she go let it in,_____ she go let it out.__

She go let it out,____ she go let it in,__

she go let it out._____

Is it a-ny won-der why prin - ces and kings___ are clowns that ca - per in their

We're the build-ers of their des - ti - ny.

So go let it out,

Verse 3:
I'm goin' leavin' the city
I'm goin' drivin' outta town
And you're comin' with me
The right time is always now.

So go let it out
And go let it in
And go let it out.
So go let it out
So go let it in
And go let it out.

Is it any wonder *etc.*

Songbird

Words & Music by Liam Gallagher

1. Talk-ing to the song-bird yes-ter-day,_____ flew me to a
(Verse 2 see block lyric, on 𝄋 instrumental ad lib.)

place not far a - way. She's a lit-tle

Verse 2:
A man can never dream these kinds of things
Especially when she came and spread her wings
Whispered in my ear the things I'd like
Then she flew away into the night.

Gonna write a song etc.

Morning Glory

Words & Music by Noel Gallagher

1. All your dreams are made when you're chained to the mir-ror with your ra-zor blade. To-day's the day that all the world will see

(Verse 2 see block lyric)

an - oth - er sun - ny af - ter - noon__

walk - ing to the sound of my fav - 'rite tune,__ to -

mor - row ne - ver knows what it does - n't know__ too soon.__

Need a lit - tle time to wake__ up,

you need a lit-tle time to wake_ up, wake_ up,
well,_____ what's the sto-ry morn -
-ing glo-ry, well,_____ you
need a lit-tle time to wake_ up, wake_ up.

Verse 2:
All your dreams are made
When you're chained to the mirror with your razor blade
Today's the day that all the world will see
Another sunny afternoon
I'm walking to the sound of my favourite tune
Tomorrow doesn't know what it doesn't know too soon.

Champagne Supernova

Words & Music by Noel Gallagher

slide, in a cham - pagne su - per - no - va, a

cham - pagne su - per - no - va in the sky.

1. Wake up the dawn and ask— her why,— a
(Verse 2 see block lyric)

dream - er dreams— she ne - ver dies,— wipe that tear a - way— now from your eyes..

92

Fmaj7 G Fmaj7 G A A/G

A/F♯ A/E A

A/G A/F♯ A/E

A A/G

How ma - ny spe - cial peo - ple change — how ma - ny lives are liv - ing strange, —

Verse 2:
How many special people change
How many lives are living strange
Where were you while we were getting high?
Slowly walking down the hall
Faster than a cannon ball
Where were you while we were getting high?

97

Don't Look Back In Anger

Words & Music by Noel Gallagher

101

Verse 2:
Take me to the place where you go
Where nobody knows if it's night or day
Please don't put your life in the hands
Of a rock 'n' roll band who'll throw it all away.

I'm gonna start a revolution from my head
'Cause you said the brains I had went to my head
Step outside, the summertime's in bloom
Stand up beside the fireplace, take that look from off your face
'Cause you ain't never gonna burn my heart out.

123456789

oasis

STOP THE CLOCKS